Niko Discovers
the 5 Senses Game

A Mindfulness Game
to Help Calm Worry and Anxiety

Written and Illustrated by Karen Correll

Karen Correll

Dedication

This book is dedicated to my amazing husband David
and our two beautiful daughters, Devon and Mackenzie.
Your love and encouragement are what fulfills my life everyday.
Thank you for all you bring into my world. I am forever grateful.

Niko is sitting on his bed. He is worried.

"Do you get worried, Mommy?" asks Niko.

"Of course, my sweet boy," says Niko's mom. "Everyone gets worried sometimes."

Relieved, Niko asks, "I feel all bunched up inside. Is there a way to stop feeling like this?"

"What you are feeling is called anxiety. It makes the muscles in your body tense, which can give you stomach aches and headaches. Anxiety also makes it difficult to focus, because your brain just wants to think about all the bad things that could happen.

"To help me calm down and not worry so much, I play a game. It's called the **5 Senses Game**. Let's go sit on the back porch. We'll play together, and I will show you," says Niko's mom.

"The five senses are the ways we use our body to learn about the world around us. We use each of these senses for learning, and we will explore each one in our game. The five senses are:

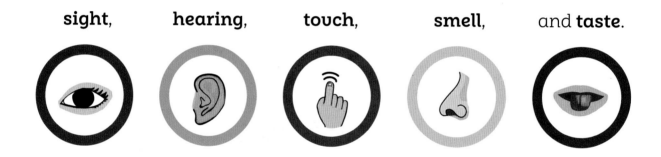

sight, **hearing,** **touch,** **smell,** and **taste.**

"The rules are easy. I am going to ask you questions, but don't tell me your answers. Just think it to yourself," says Niko's mom.

SIGHT

"We will start with the sense of **sight**. Niko, look around you and pick one thing that you see. Pick one to focus on, and nod when you are ready."

Niko looks around the yard.

He sees pretty green trees. He spies a butterfly resting on a flower. He spots a squirrel eating an acorn.

He chooses the squirrel and nods.

"Look at what you've picked. Does it look smooth or rough? Is it big or small? How does seeing this make you feel?" Niko's mom asks.

SIGHT

Niko watches the squirrel.

It has a short coat of hair on its body but long hair on its tail. The squirrel picks up fallen acorns and puts them into his mouth. It scurries up a tree.

Niko laughs. He feels happy seeing the squirrel.

HEARING

"Our second sense is **hearing**. Close your eyes and listen to all of the sounds around us."

Niko shuts his eyes and listens carefully.

He hears leaves moving on the trees. He hears an ice cream truck in the distance. He hears a bird singing.

He chooses the bird and nods.

"Is the sound loud or soft? Is the sound a high note like a whistle or a low note like a cow mooing? How does this sound make you feel?" asks Niko's mom.

HEARING

Niko listens to the bird.

The bird's song is soft but clear. The bird plays his song over and over. It's a high pitch, kind of like when Mommy whistles.

Niko smiles. He feels relaxed hearing the bird sing.

TOUCH

"The third sense is **touch**. Close your eyes and identify all of the things that you are touching or that are touching you," Niko's mom says.

He feels the wind blowing his hair around. He feels his bare feet touching the rough wood of the step. He feels water from the sprinkler on his feet.

He chooses the water from the sprinkler and nods.

"Did you choose something that you are touching or something that is touching you? Is it warm or cold? How does it make you feel?" Niko's mom asks.

TOUCH

Niko feels the water touching his feet.

When the wind blows, it creates a very light mist. It tickles his toes. When the wind blows harder, the mist reaches all the way up to his face.

Niko giggles. He feels excited waiting for the mist to come back.

"Our next sense is **smell**. With your eyes closed, take a deep breath in through your nose. What do you smell?"

Niko breathes in through his nose.

He smells freshly cut grass. He smells lillies from his mom's garden. He smells the cookies she baked for his afternoon snack.

He chooses the smell of the cookies and nods.

"Is the smell good or bad? Is it close or far away? How does this smell make you feel?" Niko's mom asks.

SMELL

Niko breathes in the smell the cookies.

He smells the peanut butter in the cookie. He smells the chocolate candy on the cookie. *Mm mmm!* He is looking forward to eating one or two at snack time.

Niko licks his lips. He feels hungry thinking of how good those cookies taste. Is it almost time for his afternoon snack?

TASTE

"Now we will move to our sense of **taste**. Think about your favorite taste," says Niko's mom.

Niko thinks about all of his favorite foods.

Grape popsicles always hit the spot. Chicken nuggets with ketchup are also one of his favorite foods. He still smells the cookies his mom baked, and that reminds him of how good they taste.

He smiles thinking of those delicious cookies. His tummy rumbles with hunger, and he nods his head quickly.

"What does that taste remind you of? When was the last time you tasted it? How does that taste make you feel?" Niko's mom asks.

TASTE

Niko almost tastes the cookies for real. It's all he can think about!

They are both sweet and nutty. He can taste the sugar that dough was rolled in. He can taste the peanut butter mixed with the chocolate candy.

Niko remembers eating those cookies last winter. He came in from playing in the snow, and his mom had prepared cookies and hot cocoa for him. That was such a fun day! *I love those cookies*, thinks Niko. He smiles as he remembers.

Niko hugs himself. He feels loved when he thinks about the taste of the cookies. He sure could go for a cookie right now!

"Niko, think about each of the five senses and each item you chose to focus on. Remember how you felt too."

Niko closes his eyes and thinks back on what he felt today.

Sight: Niko remembers he saw a squirrel. He thinks about that busy, silly squirrel and how it would stuff acorns into its cheeks. The squirrel helped him laugh.

Hearing: Niko recalls how the birds sang to each other and how they seemed to enjoy their songs. He wonders what they were saying to each other. He realizes the songbirds helped him feel happy.

Touch: When the sprinkler mist touched his toes, it tickled just a little bit. It was very refreshing, and he felt excited waiting for the wind to blow the mist onto his feet.

Smell: The smell of those yummy cookies helped Niko realize he was hungry. It also helped him feel thankful that his mom baked cookies and taught him this game.

Taste: He loves the taste of those peanut butter blossom cookies! It feels good to be loved.

Niko's mom asks one more question. "Niko, please keep your eyes closed. Complete this sentence out loud with how you feel inside now. 'My name is Niko, and I am . . .' "

"My name is Niko, and I am happy and grateful," Niko says with a grin. "And hungry!" he adds with a laugh.

"Niko, open your eyes."

He opens his eyes and sees his mom holding a glass of milk and two peanut butter blossom cookies. "Are these for me?" asks Niko, his eyes wide with hope.

"They are!" replies Niko's mom.

"Yay! Thank you!" exclaims Niko.

"You are very welcome," says Niko's mom.

"Niko, always remember that whenever you feel worried, you can play this game, even if you are alone. It is easy and fun. Just remember your fives senses. Then describe the feelings you have inside from each of the items you selected.

"Each one of the five senses help us concentrate on what is all around us. The game teaches us to focus on the moment, which helps us change our emotions from worry to calm."

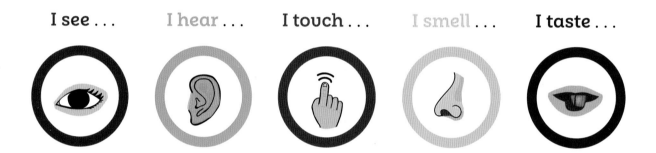

I see . . .   I hear . . .   I touch . . .   I smell . . .   I taste . . .

"That was so much fun. I feel so much better." Niko hugs his mom. "I love you."

"I love you too," says Mommy.

"I was worried before playing the **5 Senses Game**, but now I am calm! I like this feeling much better. Thank you for teaching me how to not worry so much. And for the cookies!"

Peanut Butter Blossom Cookie Recipe

Ingredients

- 1/2 cup granulated sugar
- 1/2 cup brown sugar, packed
- 1/2 cup peanut butter, creamy
- 1/2 cup butter, softened
- 1 egg
- 1 & 1/2 cup all-purpose flour
- 3/4 teaspoon baking soda
- 1/2 teaspoon baking powder
- 36 milk chocolate candies
- Note: You will need extra granulated sugar if you choose to roll the dough before adding candies.

Supplies

- ungreased cookie sheet
- large bowl
- medium bowl
- electric mixer or wooden spoon
- cooling rack

Directions

1. Preheat oven to 375°F.
2. In a large bowl, combine granulated sugar, brown sugar, peanut butter, butter, and egg. Beat with electric mixer on medium speed or mix with a spoon until well-blended.
3. In a smaller bowl, mix together flour, baking soda, and baking powder until completely combined.
4. Add the dry mixture to the wet mixture and mix well until dough forms.
5. Shape the dough into 1-inch balls. If desired, roll each ball in sugar.
6. Place the dough balls on the ungreased cookie sheet, about two inches apart.
7. Bake 8-10 minutes or until edges are a light golden brown.
8. Remove the cookie sheet from the oven and immediately press 1 milk chocolate candy into the center of each cookie. Remove the cookies from the cookie sheet and onto the cooling rack. Let cool completely before storing.

About the Author

Karen Correll lives in Vermont with her greatest love, Dave, her husband of 33 years. She treasures the time she gets to devote to Dave, their daughters, Devon and Mackenzie, and pups, Gracie and Maisy.

She has enjoyed a career in business for over 30 years. She opted to return to school to complete her undergrad degree at 53, pivoting to communications where she has thrived and will soon graduate. However, her hobbies of writing, watercolors, acrylics, and other forms of art bring her joy and peace.

As a part of her degree plan, she studied childhood anxiety. Due to the rise in childhood anxiety during the coronavirus pandemic, she began her journey to create *Niko Discovers the 5 Senses Game*. This practice helps children gain valuable mindfulness skills that are essential for their well-being and development on their journey through life.